Where am I from?

Art & Words by:

Marli van Sittert

Assistant Illustrator: Chrissie-Claudia Castraveti

Based on a true story...

Bistra, 2023

Dedicated to:

Granny / Ouma / Buni: **Donsie**

...and Chrissie's cousins:
Jack and Joe in New Zealand

ISBN: 978-973-0-39414-6

This book belongs to:

· ·

Draw your face here:

One day, Chrissie came home from kindergarten.

She had a **VERY** big question...

"Mama is from **South Africa.**

Right **down here.**

There are
lots of
wild animals.

There are super nice beaches.

...the people like to have **lots** of barbecues! They call it **'braai'**.

...and they are very **friendly and smiley!**

In South Africa Mama
spoke **Afrikaans.”**

"Hallo, hoe gaan dit?”
<Hi, how are you?>

"Daddy is from **Romania.**

Right **up here.**

...and **big brown bears** in beautiful forests.

The people have
very **interesting traditions.**

In Romania Daddy spoke

Romanian."

"Buna, ce faci?"
<Hi, how are
you?>

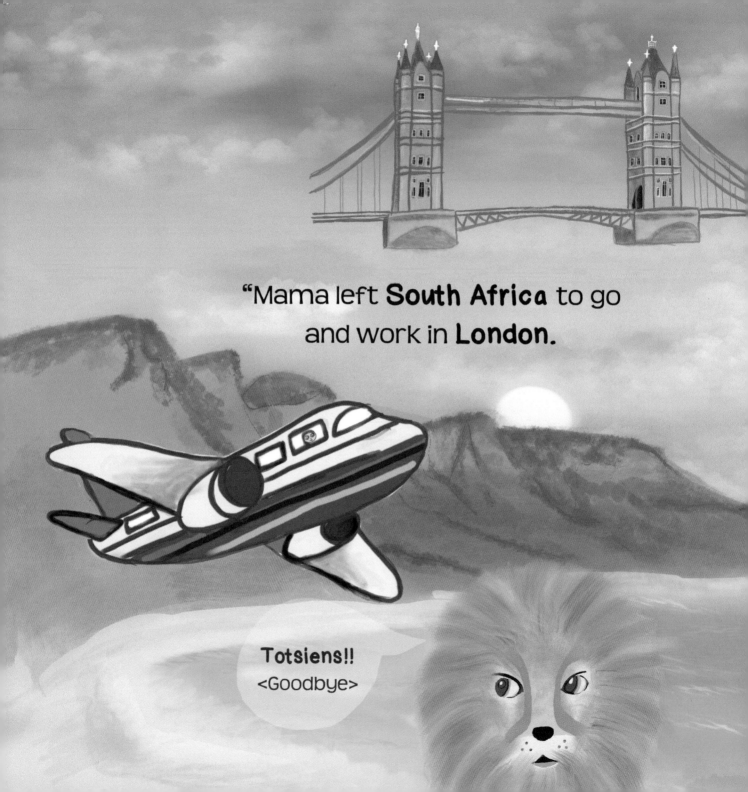

Daddy left **Romania** to go and work in **London**.

Mama and Daddy met each other in **London.**

We had to speak **English** to understand each other...

These are for you!

Oh, Thank You!

We **fell in love**...

...and we **got married**...

...and then we were **expecting** our little **Chrissie!!!**"

Do we stay in **London?**

Do we move to **Romania?**

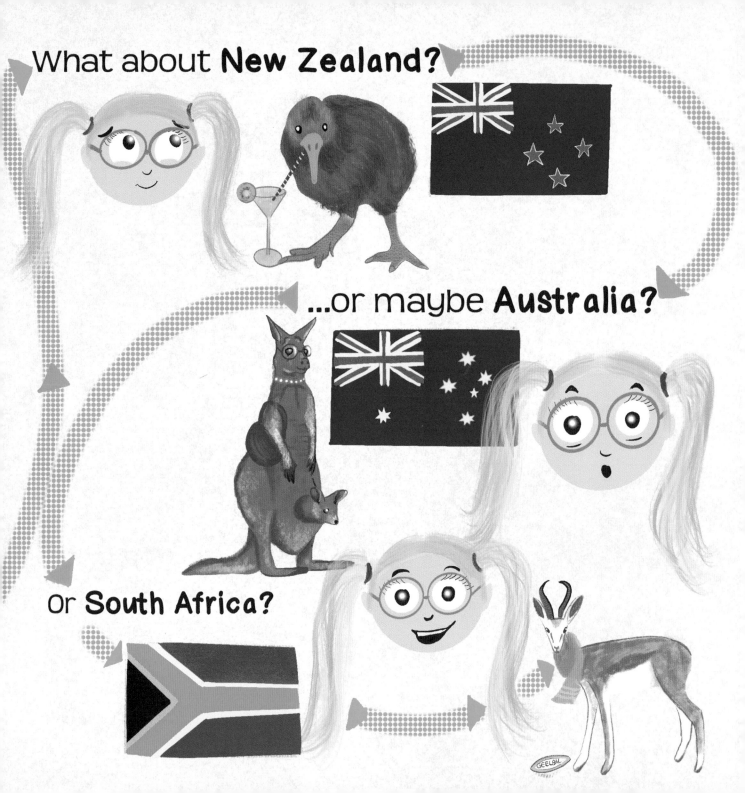

"Lots of parents all around the world have to make these difficult decisions.

The world is a **very big** place!

196 Countries!!!

...and it is important to **weigh up** and **consider** all your **options.**"

"Is that like when I have to **consider** whether **pizza or pasta** is the **best option** for me?"

"So...some families choose to live in big, fancy **city apartments.**

Some families prefer **towns**.

Some families live on **farms**.

Some families prefer life on **remote islands.**

Mamas and daddies just want what
is **best for their families.**

Your mama and daddy had a dream about living in the **beautiful mountains of Romania!**

With **lots of animals...**

Little **baby Chrissie** was **born** in **London.**

...and when you were **teeny weeny,** we moved to **Romania.**

It was **VERY** exciting!!!

So...what is **important**, is to learn the **language** of the country we move to.

cat Pisica

dog caine

MAMA

PLeasE te Rog

It is **important** to try their **food**...

MENU:
- placinte (pies)
- ciorba de fasole (bean soup)
- sarmale (cabbage rolls)
- cozonac (sweet bread)
- papanasi (cottage cheese doughnuts)

...learn about their **culture**...

ROMANIAN MASKS

...sing their **songs**...

...and try their **dances!**

It can be **tricky**, but it's **fun!!!**

...even if you sometimes fall on your bum!!!

And...I am sure your friends at school enjoy learning **English words** from you!!!"

scoala = school

"So, I am not the only kid in the world who is **different** to my friends at school?"

"No, my sweetie, **definitely not!**

There are lots of **International kiddies,** just like you!"

Meet Emilie

- Daddy from France
- Mama from South Africa
- Currently living in Luxembourg

Meet Fredrik

- Daddy from Sweden
- Mama from Denmark
- Currently living in England

Meet Daniel

-Daddy from Zimbabwe
- Mama from Nigeria
- Currently living in Ireland

Meet Sandi

- Daddy from India
- Mama from Sri Lanka
- Currently living in Italy

Meet Molly

- Daddy from Scotland
- Mama from Poland
- Currently living in New Zealand

Meet Ben

- Daddy from Germany
- Mama from China
- Currently living in Australia

Meet Bibi

- Daddy from Japan
- Mama from Spain
- Currently living in Portugal

Meet Pieter

- Daddy from Namibia
- Mama from South Africa
- Currently living in America

About The Author

Originally from Strand, South Africa, Marli is an Expat who spent 16 years in the UK, where she married her Romanian Husband. After the birth of their cheeky little girl, Chrissie, they immigrated to the stunning Carpathian Mountains where they now live in a remote village with their +/- 40 animals.

Having been an Expat for 20+ years, she knows all about the trials and tribulations of settling into a new country where you need to adapt to a new language, new culture and new way of life.

As a full time working mom (in IT), she tries to spend all her free time on art...when she is not occupied with playing Lego friends, building stuffy toy forts and dancing around like a My Little Pony!

For even more fun

Visit www.marlivansittert.com for:
- Downloadable coloring pages
- Downloadable Activity Sheets
- How to draw Flags
...and more!

A word from the author:
If you enjoyed this book, it would mean the world to me if you would take a short minute to leave a heartfelt review on Amazon. Your kind feedback will be really appreciated. Thank you so very much!
Marli

Just scan
the QR Code:

Special Extras!!!

Draw the flag of the country you were **born** in:

Grab some pencils!

Draw the flag of the country you **live** in:

...and what if all 4 flags are the same? That is pretty **awesome** too!!!

Draw the flags of the countries **your parents are from:**

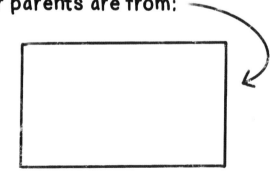

....and don't worry if it's not perfect. Flags can be super tricky sometimes!!!